The
of My School

by F. Isabel Campoy
illustrated by Ben Fine

Harcourt

Orlando   Boston   Dallas   Chicago   San Diego

Visit *The Learning Site!*

www.harcourtschool.com

My name is Juan. Let me tell you the ABCs of my new school. My family and I moved to the United States of **America**. My new school is very **big**.

Every morning, I go to my **classroom**. I sit down at my **desk**.

On Tuesdays, we play sports and
get lots of **exercise**. I have fun with
my new **friends**!

I listen carefully to what my teacher says because I want to get good **grades**. I am so **happy** when my teacher tells me I did a good job.

When it rains, we stay **inside** all day. Sometimes Mr. Green, the **janitor**, visits our classroom. Mr. Green keeps our school clean and neat.

After school, I look for my sister Consuela. She is in **kindergarten**. The chairs in her classroom are very **little**.

My favorite subject is **math**. I like to add and subtract **numbers**.

My teacher says it is **okay** to make mistakes at first. I am glad my **pencil** has a big eraser!

When I don't understand something,
I ask my teacher **questions**. I always
raise my hand before I speak.

My teacher answers my questions and gives me a big **smile**. **"Thanks** for that good question!" she says.

I wear a **uniform** to school every day. I am **very** proud to be a part of my new school.

A new boy came to our school last week. We made a big sign that said **Welcome**, **Xavier**! I think that Xavier and I will be friends.

Yesterday we went on a field trip to the **zoo**. We saw the ABCs of the zoo, from anteaters to zebras.

You can find ABCs wherever you look!

Here are the ABCs of my new school:

A - America   N - numbers
B - big   O - okay
C - classroom   P - pencil
D - desk   Q - questions
E - exercise   R - raise
F - friends   S - smile
G - grades   T - thanks
H - happy   U - uniform
I - inside   V - very
J - janitor   W - welcome
K - Kindergarten   X - Xavier
L - Little   Y - yesterday
M - math   Z - zoo